POEMS OF PRAISE

POEMS
OF PRAISE

Selected and illustrated by
PELAGIE DOANE

J. B. LIPPINCOTT COMPANY
PHILADELPHIA   NEW YORK

ACKNOWLEDGEMENTS

The editor and publisher wish to express their appreciation for permission given them to reprint the following selections.

Anonymous, "An Angel" and "Lullaby" from *Picture Rhymes from Foreign Lands,* edited by Rose Fyleman, copyright 1935 by Rose Fyleman; by permission of the publisher, J. B. Lippincott Company.

"Do You Know How Many Stars," "God Careth," "God Giveth All Things," "God Is Everywhere," "God's Gift," and "Who Taught Them" from *A Child's Thought of God,* edited by Esther Gillespie; by permission of the editor.

"The Moon" from *Poems for the Children's Hour,* edited by Josephine Bouton; by permission of the publishers, Platt and Munk Co., Inc., and Mrs. Bleecker.

Borie, Lysbeth Boyd, "Just for Jesus" from *Poems for Peter,* copyright 1928 by Lysbeth Boyd Borie; by permission of the publisher, J. B. Lippincott Company.

Buchanan, Fannie R., "The Tardy Playmate" from *Child Life Magazine,* copyright 1922; by permission of the author and *Child Life Magazine.*

Cane, Melville, "Fog, the Magician" from *The Commonweal Magazine;* by permission of *The Commonweal Magazine.*

Chesterton, Gilbert Keith, "The Christ Child" from *Wild Knight and Other Poems;* by permission of the publisher, E. P. Dutton & Co., Inc., and J. M. Dent & Sons, Ltd.

Conkling, Hilda, "Eagle on the Mountain Crest" and "Joy" from *Shoes of the Wind,* copyright 1922 by J. B. Lippincott Company; by permission of the publisher, J. B. Lippincott Company.

Davies, Mary Carolyn, "The Day before April" from *A Little Freckled Person;* by permission of the publisher, Houghton Mifflin Company.

Davies, W. H., "The Example" from *The Collected Poems of W. H. Davies;* by permission of the publisher, Jonathan Cape Limited, and Mrs. W. H. Davies.

Dickinson, Emily, "I Never Saw a Moor" from *The Poems of Emily Dickinson;* by permission of the publisher, Little, Brown & Company.

Duggan, Eileen, "Juniper" from *The Commonweal Magazine;* by permission of *The Commonweal Magazine.*

Farjeon, Eleanor, "For Christmas Day," "This Holy Night," "The Mother's Song," "The Mother's Tale," "The Riding of the Kings," and "Wildflowers" from *Eleanor Farjeon's Poems for Children,* copyright 1951 by Eleanor Farjeon; by permission of the publisher, J. B. Lippincott Company.

Farrar, John, "Prayer" from *Songs of Parents;* by permission of the publisher, Yale University Press.

Field, Eugene, "Song;" by permission of the publisher, Charles Scribner's Sons.

Fyleman, Rose, "Singing-Time" from *The Fairy Queen,* copyright 1923 by Doubleday & Co., Inc.; by permission of the publisher, Doubleday & Co., Inc., and The Society of Authors (London), and the author.

Goudge, Elizabeth, "Guardian Angel" and "In the Stable" from *Songs and Verses,* and "Thanksgiving for the Earth" from *The Little White Horse;* by permission of the author's agent, Ann Watkins.

To
Pelagie Virginia Crofton

Singing Time

I wake in the morning early
And always, the very first thing,
I poke out my head and I sit up in bed
And I sing and I sing and I sing.

Rose Fyleman

The Day before April

The day before April
    Alone, alone,
I walked in the woods
    And sat on a stone.

I sat on a broad stone
    And sang to the birds.
The tune was God's making
    But I made the words.

Mary Carolyn Davies

9

The Tardy Playmate

Good morning, sky;
Good morning, sun;
Good morning, little winds that run!
Good morning, birds;
Good morning, trees;
And creeping grass, and brownie bees!
How did you find out it was day?
Who told you night had gone away?
I'm wide awake;
I'm up now, too.
I'll be right out to play with you!

Fannie R. Buchanan

THE YEAR'S AT THE SPRING

The year's at the spring,
And day's at the morn;
Morning's at seven;
The hillside's dew-pearled;
The lark's on the wing;
The snail's on the thorn:
God's in his heaven—
All's right with the world!

Robert Browning

JOY

Joy is not a thing you can see.
It is what you feel when you watch
    waves breaking,
Or when you peer through a net of woven
    violet stems
In Spring grass.
It is not sunlight, not moonlight,
But a separate shining.
Joy lives behind people's eyes.

Hilda Conkling

Spring

All happy and glad in the sunshine I stood.
For isn't spring lovely and isn't God good?

Daniel A. Lord

An Angel Singing

I heard an Angel singing
When the day was springing,
"Mercy, Pity, Peace
Is the world's release."

Thus he sung all day
Over the new mown hay,
Till the sun went down
And haycocks looked brown.

William Blake

THE EXAMPLE

Here's an example from
   A Butterfly;
That on a rough, hard rock
   Happy can lie;
Friendless and all alone
On this unsweetened stone.

Now let my bed be hard,
   No care take I;
I'll make my joy like this
   Small Butterfly;
Whose happy heart has power
To make a stone a flower.

W. H. Davies

13

PRAYER FOR A CHILD

When it gets dark the birds and flowers
Shut up their eyes and say goodnight,
And God who loves them counts the hours,
And keeps them safe till it gets light.
Dear Father, count the hours tonight
While I'm asleep and cannot see:
And in the morning may the light
Shine for the birds, the flowers and me.

William Hawley Smith

In the Morning

When, in the morning, fresh from sleep,
I from my open window peep,
I always find some new surprise
To greet my grateful, wondering eyes.

I like to kneel and say my prayers
Before I hurry down the stairs—
Before the breakfast bell has gone—
And thank the Lord for all He's done.

While I was sleeping peacefully,
The Lord was working hard for me,
Making another lovely day
So I could stay outdoors and play.

Hundreds of daisies new and sweet
He's spread like stars around my feet.
And, knowing what I like the best,
He's put new birdlings in a nest.

Such heav'nly things He loves to do
For little folks like me and you.
I often wonder, while I play,
When does He take His holiday?

Cecilia Loftus

15

ARBOR DAY

On Arbor Day
We think of birds and greening trees,
Of meadowlands and humming bees,
Of orchards far from crowded town,
Of heights where streams go tumbling down,
Wee mountain rills that sing and play—
On Arbor Day.

Of how the tree tops coax the rain
From flying clouds till hill and plain
Are clean and fresh from sea to sea;
We plant a seed; a tiny tree
Wakes up and throws aside the clod,
And stretches for the climb toward God—
We sing a song for the joy of May—
On Arbor Day.

Annette Wynne

Fern Song

Dance to the beat of the rain, little Fern,
   And spread out your palms again,
   And say, "Though the sun
   Hath my vesture spun,
He had labored, alas, in vain
   But for the shade
   That the Cloud hath made
And the gift of the Dew and the Rain."
   Then laugh and upturn
   All your fronds, little Fern,
And rejoice in the beat of the rain!

John Bannister Tabb

God's House

God's house is wide and very tall,
The mountains serve Him for a wall;
The roof is arched and blue and high,
And starry-studded—it's the sky!

God's house is beautiful with light,
By day and night He keeps it bright;
He loves His house; He built it all—
The sky, the sea, the mountain-wall.

God's house is open wide, and free,
He lets us live here, you and me,
And we who love His house may tell
Of God's house that He built so well.

Annette Wynne

God Is Everywhere

There's not a tint that paints the rose
   Or decks the lily fair,
Or marks the humblest flower that grows,
   But God has placed it there.

There's not a star whose twinkling light
   Illumes the spreading earth;
There's not a cloud, so dark or bright,
   But wisdom gave it birth.

There's not a place on earth's vast round,
   In ocean's deep or air,
Where love and beauty are not found,
   For God is everywhere.

Anonymous

How Nice!

How nice it is, dear God, to know
That You make all the flowers grow!
How nice it is to stop and think
You made the spring from which I drink!
How nice it is to know that You
Painted the sky that lovely blue!
How nice it is to know You fill
The night with stars and always will!
But O! How nice to know You made
Me, too! Sometimes I am afraid
I do not thank You as I should—
You are so wise, dear God, and good!

Mary Dixon Thayer

20

OUT IN THE FIELDS WITH GOD

The little cares that fretted me
  I lost them yesterday,
Among the fields above the sea,
  Among the winds at play,
Among the lowing of the herds,
  The rustling of the trees,
Among the singing of the birds,
  The humming of the bees.

The foolish fears of what might happen,
  I cast them all away
Among the clover-scented grass,
  Among the new-mown hay,
Among the husking of the corn,
  Where drowsy poppies nod
Where ill thoughts die and good are born—
  Out in the fields with God.

Anonymous

The Country Faith

Here in the country's heart
Where the grass is green,
Life is the same sweet life
As it e'er hath been.

Trust in a God still lives,
And the bell at morn
Floats with a thought of God
O'er the rising corn.

God comes down in the rain,
And the crop grows tall—
This is the country faith,
And best of all!

Norman Gale

Revelation

Down in the meadow, spread with dew
    I saw the Very God
Look from a flower's limpid blue,
    Child of a starveling sod.

Alice Brown

Boats Sail on the Rivers

Boats sail on the rivers,
  And ships sail on the seas;
But clouds that sail across the sky
  Are prettier far than these.

There are bridges on the rivers,
  As pretty as you please;
But the bow that bridges heaven,
  And overtops the trees,
And builds a road from earth to sky,
  Is prettier far than these.

Christina Rossetti

23

Thanksgiving for the Earth

Praised be our Lord for our brother the sun,
Most comely is he, and bright,
Praised be our Lord for our sister the moon,
With her pure and lovely light.
Praised be our Lord for the sparkling bright stars
Encircling the dome of night.

Praised be our Lord for the wind and the rain,
For clouds, for dew and the air;
For the rainbow set in the sky above
Most precious and kind and fair.
For all these things tell the love of our Lord,
The love that is everywhere.

Praised be our Lord for our Mother the earth,
Most gracious is she, and good.
With her gifts of flowers and nuts and fruit,
Of grass and corn and wood.
For she it is who upholds us in life
And gives us our daily food.

Praised be our Lord for the turn of the year,
For new-born life upspringing;
For buds and for blossoms, for lambs and babes,
For thrush and blackbird singing.
May praise, like the lark, leap up from our hearts,
To heaven's gate upwinging.

Elizabeth Goudge

Time to Go

They know the time to go!
The fairy clocks strike their inaudible hour
In field and woodland, and each punctual flower
Bows at the signal an obedient head
  And hastes to bed.

The pale Anemone
Glides on her way with scarcely a good night;
The violets in their purple nightcaps tight;
Hand clasped in hand, the dancing Columbines.
  In blithesome lines,

Drop their last courtesies,
Flit from the scene, and couch them for their rest:
The Meadow Lily folds her scarlet vest
And hides it 'neath the Grasses' lengthening green;
  Fair and serene,

Her sister Lily floats
On the blue pond, and raises golden eyes
To court the golden splendor of the skies—
The sudden signal comes, and down she goes
    To find repose,

In the cool depths below.
A little later, and the Asters blue
Depart in crowds, a brave and cheery crew;
While Goldenrod, still wide awake and gay,
    Turns him away,

Furls his bright parasol,
And like a little hero, meets his fate.
The Gentians, very proud to·sit up late,
Next follow. Every Fern is tucked and set
    'Neath coverlet,

Downy and soft and warm.
No little seedling voice is heard to grieve
Or make complaints the folding woods beneath;
No lingerer dares to stay, for well they know
    The time to go.

Teach us your patience, brave,
Dear flowers, till we shall dare to part like you,
Willing God's will, sure that His clock strikes true,
    With smiles, not sorrow.

Susan Coolidge

GOD CARETH

Something around which it may twine
    God gives every little vine.

Some little nook or sunny bower
    God gives every little flower.

Some green bough or mossy sward
    God gives every little bird.

Night and day, at home, abroad,
    Little ones are safe with God.

Anonymous

TODAY

So here hath been dawning
  Another blue day:
Think, wilt thou let it
  Slip useless away?

Out of Eternity
  This new day is born;
Into Eternity
  At night will return.

Behold it afore time,
  No eye ever did:
So soon it forever
  From all eyes is hid.

Here hath been dawning
  Another blue day;
Think, wilt thou let it
  Slip useless away?

Thomas Carlyle

Flower in the Crannied Wall

Flower in the crannied wall,
I pluck you out of the crannies,
I hold you here, root and all, in my hand,
Little flower—but if I could understand
What you are, root and all, and all in all,
I should know what God and man is.

Alfred, Lord Tennyson

God gives so many lovely things!
He gives the bird its feathery wings,
The butterfly its colors fair,
The bee a velvet coat to wear.

He gives the garden all its flowers,
And sun to make them grow, and showers;
Red apples for the old bent tree,
Wheat in the meadow blowing free;

Cool grass upon the summer hills,
And silvery streams to turn the mills.
He gives the shining day, and then
The quiet, starry night again.

He gives my home—a place to stay,
And laugh, and dream, and work, and play,
The pleasant rooms and windows wide,
And cozy, rosy fireside;

And books to read and folks to love me,
And His good care to watch above me.
It's like a song a person sings—
God gives so many happy things!

Nancy Byrd Turner

WILDFLOWERS

We mustn't pick the garden flowers
　　Because they've got a wall round them,
But wildflowers in the grass are ours
　　With woods and meadows all round them.

The buttercups and daisies stand
　　And wait for us to play with them,
And primroses on every hand
　　Ask us to go away with them.

The bluebell and the daffodil
　　Belong to all who feel for them,
The cowslips growing on the hill
　　Are yours if you will kneel for them.

The willowherb, the gold kingcup,
　　Are his who seeks the brook for them,
And violets are for picking up
　　If you will only look for them.

The garden flowers inside the wall
　　Belong to him who planted them,
But God once sowed the wildflowers all
　　For anyone who wanted them.

Eleanor Farjeon

If All the Skies

If all the skies were sunshine,
Our faces would be fain
To feel once more upon them
The cooling plash of rain.

If all the world were music,
Our hearts would often long
For one sweet strain of silence,
To break the endless song.

If life were always merry,
Our souls would seek relief,
And rest from weary laughter
In the quiet arms of grief.

Henry VanDyke

THE GOLDEN RULE

The Golden Rule is the Rule of Three,
It really means God, and my neighbor,
and me.

Annette Wynne

FOUR THINGS

Four things a man must learn to do
If he would make his record true;
To think without confusion clearly,
To love his fellow men sincerely;
To act from honest motives purely;
To trust in God and Heaven securely.

Henry VanDyke

I WILL GIVE YOU

I will give you the end of a golden
    string,
    Only wind it into a ball,
It will lead you in at heaven's gate
Built in Jerusalem's Wall.

William Blake

Do You Know How Many Stars?

Do you know how many stars
There are shining in the sky?
Do you know how many clouds
Ev'ry day go floating by?
God in heaven has counted all,
He would miss one should it fall.

Do you know how many children
Go to little beds at night,
And without a care or sorrow,
Wake up in the morning light?
God in heaven each name can tell,
Loves you too, and loves you well.

From the German

The Stars

What do the stars do
   Up in the sky,
Higher than the wind can blow
   Or the clouds fly?

Each star in its own glory
   Circles, circles still;
As it was lit to shine and set
   And do its Master's will.

Christina Rossetti

Sky so bright
Blue and light,
Stars how many hast thou?
    Countless stars.
Countless times
Shall our God be praised now.

Forest green,
Cool, serene,
Leaves how many hast thou?
    Countless leaves.
Countless times
Shall our God be praised now.

Deepest sea,
Wide and free,
Waves how many hast thou?
    Countless waves.
Countless times
Shall our God be praised now.

Eternity,
Eternity,
Hours how many hast thou?
    Countless hours.
Countless times
Shall our God be praised now,
Shall our God be praised now.

Anonymous

NIGHT

The sun descending in the west,
  The evening star does shine;
The birds are silent in their nest,
  And I must seek for mine.
    The moon, like a flower
    In heaven's high bower,
    With silent delight
    Sits and smiles on the night.

Farewell, green fields and happy grove,
    Where flocks have ta'en delight;
Where lambs have nibbled, silent move
    The feet of angels bright;
        Unseen they pour blessing,
        And joy without ceasing,
        On each bud and blossom,
        And each sleeping bosom.

They look in every thoughtless nest,
    Where birds are cover'd warm,
They visit caves of every beast,
    To keep them all from harm:—
        If they see any weeping
        That should have been sleeping
        They pour sleep on their head,
        And sit down by their bed.

William Blake

THE MOON

I see the moon,
And the moon sees me;
God bless the moon,
And God bless me.

Celtic Child's Saying

The Whisperer

The moon was round,
And as I walked along
There was no sound,
Save where the wind with long
Low hushes whispered to the ground
  A snatch of song.

No thought had I
Save that the moon was fair,
And fair the sky,
And God was everywhere.
I chanted as the wind went by
  A poet's prayer.

James Stephens

NIGHT

Stars over snow,
  And in the west a planet
Swinging below a star—
  Look for a lovely thing and
    you will find it,
It is not far—
  It never will be far.

Sara Teasdale

Things to Remember

A robin redbreast in a cage
Puts all Heaven in a rage.

A skylark wounded on the wing,
A cherubim does cease to sing.

He who shall hurt the little wren
Shall never be beloved by men.

The wanton boy that kills the fly
Shall feel the spider's enmity.

A truth that's told with bad intent
Beats all the lies you can invent.

William Blake

SHEEP AND LAMBS

All in the April morning,
  April airs were abroad;
The sheep with their little lambs
  Passed me by on the road.

The sheep with their little lambs
  Passed me by on the road;
All in an April evening
  I thought on the Lamb of God.

The lambs were weary, and crying
  With a weak human cry,
I thought on the Lamb of God
  Going meekly to die.

Up in the blue, blue mountains
  Dewy pastures are sweet:
Rest for the little bodies,
  Rest for the little feet.

All in the April evening,
  April airs were abroad;
I saw the sheep with their lambs,
  And thought on the Lamb of God.

Katharine Tynan Hinkson

THE LAMB

Little Lamb, who made thee?
Dost thou know who made thee?
Gave thee life, and bid thee feed
By the stream and o'er the mead;
Gave thee clothing of delight,
Softest clothing, woolly, bright;
Gave thee such a tender voice,
Making all the vales rejoice?
Little Lamb, who made thee?
Dost thou know who made thee?

Little Lamb, I'll tell thee,
Little Lamb, I'll tell thee:
He is called by thy name,
For He calls Himself a Lamb.
He is meek, and He is mild;
He became a little child.
I a child, and thou a lamb,
We are called by His name.
Little Lamb, God bless thee!
Little Lamb, God bless thee!

William Blake

EAGLE ON THE MOUNTAIN CREST

His bronze shone like a haze:
From below you would think him an image
Of long ago.
But he is real . . . he is of now-a-days:
No one made him but God.

Hilda Conkling

THE TIGER

Tiger, tiger, burning bright
In the forest of the night!
What immortal hand or eye
Could frame thy fearful symmetry?

In what distant deeps or skies
Burnt the ardour of thine eyes?
On what wings dare he aspire—
What the hand dare seize the fire?

And what shoulder, and what art
Could twist the sinews of thy heart?
And when thy heart began to beat,
What dread hand form'd thy dread feet?

What the hammer, what the chain,
In what furnace was thy brain?
Did God smile his work to see?
Did He who made the lamb make thee?

William Blake

The Voice of God

I bent unto the ground
And I heard the quiet sound
Which the grasses make when they
Come up laughing from the clay.

"We are the voice of God," they said:
Thereupon I bent my head
Down again that I might see
If they truly spoke to me.

But around me everywhere
Grass and tree and mountain were
Thundering in a mighty glee,
"We are the voice of deity."

And I leapt from where I lay,
I danced upon the laughing clay,
And to the rock that sang beside,
"We are the voice of God," I cried.

James Stephens

WHO TAUGHT THEM?

Who taught the bird to build her nest
    Of softest wool and hay and moss,
Who taught her how to weave it best,
    And lay the tiny twigs across?

Who taught the busy bee to fly
    Among the sweetest herbs and flowers;
And lay her store of honey by,
    Providing food for winter hours?

Who taught the little ant the way
    Her narrow hole so well to bore?
And through the pleasant summer day,
    To gather up her winter's store?

'Twas God that taught them all the way,
    And gave these little creatures skill;
And teaches children, if they pray,
    To know and do His holy will.

                                    Anonymous

It Was Saint Francis Who Came

It was Saint Francis who came,
But we did not know his name;
We gave him coffee and bread.
"I must save some food for the birds," he
    said;
"The poor little birds, and winter is here—"
And all of the sparrows came flying near;

They liked that man, they knew him before.
It was Saint Francis came to the door;
His coat was old, and his hat was queer.
But he has birds for friends all through the
   year.

Annette Wynne

Fog, the Magician

Wrapped in a cloak
Of grey mystery,
Fog, the magician,
Steals tip-toe out of the sea.
In seven-league boots
He skims across the sky,
Blowing out the sun,
Blotting out the blue.

On cobweb wires he slides to earth,
Glides through gardens surreptitiously,
And sponges every color out of flowers.
Churches, houses, trees,
He wipes like chalky outlines from a board.

Fog says—"Presto!"
And birds turn into nothing as they fly,
Men grow vague and vanish.
Fog claps his hands!
And motorcars roll off into a void,
Dogs evaporate,
Cats dissolve to bodiless meows.
Noiselessly, peacefully,
The old world ends.
Nothing remains
But fog and me
And another world to be.
Slowly, dimly,
I seem to feel
A little of the wonder and the joy
That must have gladdened God in the beginning—
Creation before Him.

Melville Cane

CRAYONS

You ask me how God felt on that first day.
I think I know:
With paper and a new box of bright crayons
I have felt just so—
The children pressing at each elbow
("Draw a sunset and a polar bear!")
. . . But even God was not so lucky—
He had no audience there.

Christopher Morley

A Little Song of Life

Glad that I live am I;
　That the sky is blue;
Glad for the country lanes,
　And the fall of dew.

After the sun the rain,
　After the rain the sun;
This is the way of life,
　Till the work be done.

All that we need to do,
　Be we low or high,
Is to see that we grow
　Nearer the sky.

Lizette Woodworth Reese

Auguries of Innocence

To see the world in a grain of sand,
　And a heaven in a wild flower;
Hold infinity in the palm of your hand,
　And eternity in an hour.

William Blake

POEM FOR A CHILD

The rabbit came bounding,
And the shaggy bear,
For a run with their master;
But no one was there!

The dew of the morning
Was about their feet
And the garden as ever
Was sunlit and sweet.

But no one made answer
To the heartbroken cry,
And the slow-pacing lion
Went, wondering, by.

They searched all the garden
To the farthest ends
While the rabbit kept asking:
Where are our friends?

"Lord Adam who named us
And the Lady Eve?
They have left us forever
To seek and to grieve."

The angel who guarded
With a shining sword
The strait gateway of Eden
Would give them no word.

But out of far Heaven
When the hour grew late
Came a voice, full of pity,
Whispering, "Wait."

J. G. E. Hopkins

THE CREATION

All things bright and beautiful,
All creatures, great and small,
All things wise and wonderful,
The Lord God made them all.

Each little flower that opens,
Each little bird that sings,
He made their glowing colors,
He made their tiny wings;

The rich man in his castle,
The poor man at his gate,
God made them, high or lowly,
And ordered their estate.

The purple-headed mountain,
The river running by,
The sunset and the morning
That brightens up the sky;

The cold wind in the winter,
The pleasant summer sun,
The ripe fruits in the garden—
He made them every one.

The tall trees in the greenwood,
  The meadows where we play,
The rushes by the water
  We gather every day—

He gave us eyes to see them,
  And lips that we might tell
How great is God Almighty
  Who has made all things well!

Cecil Frances Alexander

I Never Saw a Moor

I never saw a moor,
I never saw the sea;
Yet know I how the heather looks,
And what a wave must be.

I never spoke with God,
Nor visited in heaven;
Yet certain am I of the spot
As if the chart were given.

Emily Dickinson

PARADISE

Once in a dream I saw the flowers
  That bud and bloom in Paradise;
  More fair are they than waking eyes
Have seen in all this world of ours.
And faint the perfume-bearing rose,
  And faint the lily on its stem,
And faint the perfect violet,
  Compared with them.

I heard the songs of paradise;
  Each bird sat singing in its place;
  A tender song so full of grace
It soared like incense to the skies.
Each bird sat singing to its mate
  Soft cooing notes among the trees:
The nightingale herself were cold
  To such as these.

I saw the fourfold River flow,
    And deep it was, with golden sand;
    It flowed between a mossy land
With murmured music grave and low.
It hath refreshment for all thirst,
    For fainting spirits strength and rest:
Earth holds not such a draught as this
    From east to west.

The Tree of Life stood budding there,
    Abundant with its twelvefold fruits;
    Eternal sap sustains its roots,
Its shadowing branches fill the air.
Its leaves are healing for the world,
    Its fruit the hungry world can feed
Sweeter than honey to the taste
    And balm indeed.

I saw the Gate called Beautiful;
    And looked, but scarce could look within;
    I saw the golden streets begin,
And outskirts of the glassy pool.
Oh harps, oh crowns of plenteous stars,
    Oh green palm branches, many-leaved—
Eye hath not seen, nor ear hath heard,
    Nor heart conceived.

I hope to see these things again,
But not as once in dreams by night;
To see them with my very sight,
And touch and handle and attain:
To have all heaven beneath my feet
For narrow way that once they trod;
To have my part with all the saints
And with my God.

Christina Rossetti

REALITY

Love thy God and love Him only:
And thy breast will ne'er be lonely.
In that one great Spirit meet
All things mighty, grave and sweet.

Sir Audrey de Vere

HE PRAYETH BEST

He prayeth best who loveth best
  All things, both great and small.
For the dear Lord who loveth us,
  He made and loveth all.

Samuel Taylor Coleridge

THE SEARCH

I sought his love in sun and stars,
    And where the wild seas roll,
And found it not. As mute I stood,
    Fear overwhelmed my soul;
But when I gave to one in need,
I found the Lord of Love indeed.

I sought his love in lore of books,
    In charts of science' skill;
They left me orphaned as before—
    His love eluded still;
Then in despair I breathed a prayer;
The Lord of Love was standing there!

Thomas Curtis Clarke

The World's Music

The world's a very happy place,
  Where every child should dance and sing,
And always have a smiling face,
  And never sulk for anything.

I waken when the morning's come,
  And feel the air and light alive
With strange sweet music like the hum
  Of bees above their busy hive.

The linnets play among the leaves
  At hide-and-seek, and chirp and sing;
While, flashing to and from the eaves,
  The swallows twitter on the wing.

The twigs that shake, and boughs that sway;
  And tall old trees you could not climb;
And winds that come, but cannot stay,
  Are gaily singing all the time.

From dawn to dark the old millwheel
  Makes music, going round and round;
And dusty white with flour and meal,
  The miller whistles to its sound.

The brook that flows beside the mill,
  As happy as a brook can be,
Goes singing its own song until
  It learns the singing of the sea.

For every wave upon the sands
  Sings songs you never tire to hear,
Of laden ships from sunny lands,
  Where it is summer all the year

And if you listen to the rain
  When leaves and birds and bees are dumb,
You hear it pattering on the pane
  Like Andrew beating on his drum.

The coals beneath the kettle croon,
  And clap their hands and dance in glee;
And even the kettle hums a tune
  To tell you when it's time for tea.

The world is such a happy place
  That children, whether big or small,
Should always have a smiling face,
  And never, never, sulk at all.

Gabriel Setoun

A Child's Thought of God

They say that God lives very high!
   But if you look above the pines
You cannot see our God. And why?

And if you dig down in the mines
   You never see Him in the gold,
Though from Him all that's glory shines.

God is so good, He wears a fold
   Of heaven and earth across His face
Like secrets kept, for love untold.

But still I feel that His embrace
   Slides down by thrills, through all things made,
Through sight and sound of every place:

As if my tender mother laid
   On my shut lids her kisses' pressure,
Half-waking me at night and said,
   "Who kissed you through the dark, dear guesser?"

Elizabeth Barret Browning

God Is So Good

God is so good that He will hear,
    Whenever children humbly pray;
He always lends a gracious ear
    To what the youngest child may say.

His own most holy Book declares
    He loves good little children still;
And that He listens to their prayers,
    Just as a tender father will.

Jane Taylor

A PRAYER

Teach me, Father, how to go
Softly as the grasses grow;
Hush my soul to meet the shock
Of the wild world as a rock;
But my spirit, propt with power,
Make as simple as a flower.
Let the dry heart fill its cup,
Like a poppy looking up;
Let life lightly wear her crown,
Like a poppy looking down.

Teach me, Father, how to be
Kind and patient as a tree.
Joyfully the crickets croon
Under shady oak at noon;
Beetle, on his mission bent,
Tarries in that cooling tent.
Let me, also, cheer a spot,
Hidden field or garden grot—
Place where passing souls can rest
On the way and be their best.

Edwin Markham

Round the Clock

Up in the morning, out of bed,
   Face all washed,
And prayers all said,
   Breakfast all eaten,
Parents kissed, everything done
   And nothing missed . . .

Out on the playground,
   Games all played,
Friends all met, and plans all laid,
   Lunch all eaten, songs all sung,
Classes attended
   When bells were rung . . .

Up in the bedroom, day all done,
   Tasks are finished, and races run,
Prayers all finished,
   And books all read—
Happy the day!
   Thank God for bed.

Daniel A. Lord

THE EYES OF GOD

God watches o'er us all the day,
At home, at school and at our play;
And when the sun has left the skies
He watches with a million eyes.

Gabriel Setoun

GOOD NIGHT PRAYER

Bless my friends, the whole world bless,
Help me to learn helpfulness;
Keep me ever in thy sight,
So to all I say good night.

Henry Johnstone

GOOD NIGHT

Good night! Good night!
Far flies the light;
But still God's love
Shall flame above,
Making all bright.
Good night! Good night!

Victor Hugo

GOD'S DARK

The Dark is kind and cozy;
   The Dark is soft and deep;
The Dark will pat my pillow
   And love me as I sleep.

The Dark is smooth as velvet,
   And gentle as the air,
And he is good to children
   And people everywhere.

The Dark can see and love me
   Without a bit of light.
He gives me dreams and resting;
   He brings the gentle night.

God made the Dark, so Daytime
   Could close its tired eyes
And sleep a while in comfort
   Beneath the starry skies.

The Daytime, just like children,
   Needs rest from work and play,
So it can give us children
   Another happy day.

God made the Dark for children
   And birdies in their nest.
All in the dark He watches
   And guards us while we rest.

John Martin

GUARDIAN ANGEL

Over in the corner there's a Person standing,
There, by the doorway, and he won't let bad things pass.
He's a laughing Person, friendly and all twinkly,
Like the stars beyond the window and the frost upon the grass.

He's a shiny Person, glowing like a candle,
So you can't be frightened however dark the night,
And he says God lights him, and he says God clothes him,
So you cannot wonder at it that his raiment is so bright.

He's a winged Person, and his wings are downy,
Like feathered clouds you see at dawning of the day.
Yet they are strong too, and tapered all for swiftness;
Though he's promised on his honour he will never fly away.

He's a singing Person, who sings nice cradle songs,
Like Mother-Mary sang to Jesus at her breast.
Now and then his voice goes loud, just like a trumpet,
Though he tries to keep it Mary-soft, he tries his very best.

But he's a strong Person, a very strong Person,
Who has to fight nightmares, the bogies and the dark.
He wears golden armour, a shield and a broadsword,
And the helmet on his shiny head is crested like a lark.

Elizabeth Goudge

A Prayer for a Little Home

God send us a little home,
To come back to, when we roam.

Low walls, and fluted tiles,
Wide windows, a view for miles.

Red firelight and deep chairs,
Small white beds upstairs—

Great talk in little nooks,
Dim colors, rows of books.

One picture on each wall,
Not many things at all.

God send us a little ground,
Tall trees standing round.

Homely flowers in brown sod.
Overhead, thy stars, O God!

God bless, when winds blow,
Our home, and all we know.

Florence Bone

AN EVENING HYMN FOR A LITTLE FAMILY

Now condescend, Almighty King,
   To bless this little throng;
And kindly listen while we sing
   Our pleasant evening song.

Before Thy sacred footstool, see
   We bend in humble prayer,
A happy little family,
   To ask Thy tender care.

May we in safety sleep tonight,
   From every danger free,
Because the darkness and the light,
   Are both alike to Thee.

Ann and Jane Taylor

Evening Hymn

I hear no voice, I feel no touch,
    I see no glory bright;
But yet I know that God is near,
    In darkness as in light.

He watches ever by my side,
    And hears my whispered prayer:
The Father for His little child
    Both night and day doth care.

Anonymous

The Mystery

He came and took me by the hand
    Up to a red rose tree,
He kept His meaning to Himself,
    But gave a rose to me.

I did not pray Him to lay bare
    The mystery to me;
Enough the rose was heaven to smell,
    And His own face to see.

Ralph Hodgson

Sweet Story of Old

I think when I read that sweet story of old,
  When Jesus was here among men,
How He called little children as lambs to His fold,
  I should like to have been with them then.

I wish that His hands had been placed on my head,
  That His arm had been thrown around me,
And that I might have seen His kind look when He said,
  "Let the little ones come unto me."

Jemima Luke

GOD'S GIFT

For life and health and strength
   I thank the Father kind;
I cannot count His mercies o'er,
   So many gifts I find.

The wee bird has its nest,
   Safe in the trees so tall,
For birdlings' nests, for children's homes,
   I thank the Lord for all.

Anonymous

GOD GIVETH ALL THINGS

We thank our loving Father God,
Who gives us everything,
Who sends the sunshine and the showers,
And makes rich harvest spring.
He clothes the lilies of the field,
He feeds each bird and beast;
And all may share His tender care,
The greatest and the least.

Anonymous

An Ancient Prayer

Give me a good digestion, Lord, and also something to
  digest;
Give me a healthy body, Lord, and sense to keep it at its
  best.
Give me a healthy mind, good Lord, to keep the good and
  pure in sight,
Which, seeing sin, is not appalled, but finds a way to set
  it right.

Give me a mind that is not bound, that does not whimper,
  whine or sigh.
Don't let me worry overmuch about the fussy thing called I.
Give me a sense of humor, Lord; give me the grace to see a
  joke,
To get some happiness from life and pass it on to other folk.

Thomas H. B. Webb

83

LULLABY

Fourteen angels round my bed,
Watch beside me through the night;
Two at my feet, two at my head,
Two at my left, two at my right,
Two to cover me, two to wake me,
Two to Paradise to take me.

From the Flemish

AN ANGEL

An angel came as I lay in bed;
"I will give you wings," the angel said;
"I will give you wings that you may fly
To the country of Heaven above the sky."

My beautiful angel flew away,
He came not again by night or by day;
Angels are busy with many things,
And he has forgotten to send the wings.

From the Hebrew

Rain

Since rain is good for crops in May,
  The farmers bless a rainy day.
But so do I. Thank God who made
  The puddles where a child can wade.

Daniel A. Lord

I thank you, God,
For a hundred things:
For the flower that blooms,
For the bird that sings,
For the sun that shines,
And the rain that drops,
For ice cream,
        and raisins,
          and lollypops,
          AMEN.

Ilo Orleans

THANKS

Thank you very much indeed,
River, for your waving reed;
Hollyhocks, for budding knobs;
Foxgloves, for your velvet fobs;
Pansies, for your silky cheeks;
Chaffinches, for singing beaks;
Spring, for wood anemones
Near the mossy toes of trees;
Summer, for the fruited pear,
Yellowing crab, and cherry fare;
Autumn, for the bearded load,
Hazelnuts along the road;
Winter, for the fairy tale,
Spitting log and bouncing hail.

But, blest Father, high above,
All these joys are from Thy love;
And Your children, everywhere,
Born in palace, lane, or square,
Cry with voices all agreed,
"Thank You very much indeed."

Norman Gale

JUST FOR JESUS

Jesus, I kneel down to say
Thank you for another day,

For hands to feel and eyes to see
And all your loving gifts to me.

Teach me in your words to talk
Help me in your ways to walk,

Guide and bless me from above,
Jesus, it is you I love!

Lysbeth Boyd Borie

Loving Jesus

Loving Jesus, meek and mild,
Look upon a little child!

Make me gentle as Thou art,
Come and live within my heart.

Take my childish hand in Thine,
Guide these little feet of mine.

So shall all my happy days
Sing their pleasant song of praise;

And the world shall always see
Christ, the Holy Child, in me.

Charles Wesley

Ex Ore Infantium

Little Jesus, wast Thou shy
Once, and just so small as I?
And what did it feel like to be
Out of Heaven, and just like me?
Didst Thou sometimes think of there,
And ask where all the angels were?
I should think that I would cry
For my house all made of sky;
I would look about the air,
And wonder where my angels were;
And at waking 'twould distress me—
Not an angel there to dress me!

Hadst Thou ever any toys,
Like us little girls and boys?
And didst Thou play in Heaven with all
The angels, that were not too tall,
With stars for marbles? Did the things
Play Can you see me? through their wings?
Didst Thou kneel at night to pray,
And didst Thou join Thy hands, this way?
And did they tire sometimes, being young,
And make the prayer seem very long?
And dost Thou like it best, that we
Should join our hands to pray to Thee?
I used to think, before I knew,
The prayer not said unless we do.
And did Thy Mother at the night
Kiss Thee, and fold the clothes in right?
And didst Thou feel quite good in bed,
Kissed and sweet, and Thy prayers said?

Thou canst not have forgotten all
That it feels like to be small;
And Thou know'st I cannot pray
To Thee in my father's way—
When Thou wast so little, say,
Couldst Thou talk Thy Father's way?
So, a little Child, come down
And hear a child's tongue like Thy own;
Take me by the hand and walk,
And listen to my baby-talk.
To Thy Father show my prayer
(He will look, Thou art so fair),
And say: "O Father, I, Thy Son,
Bring the prayer of a little one."
And He will smile, that children's tongue
Hast not changed since Thou wast young!

Francis Thompson

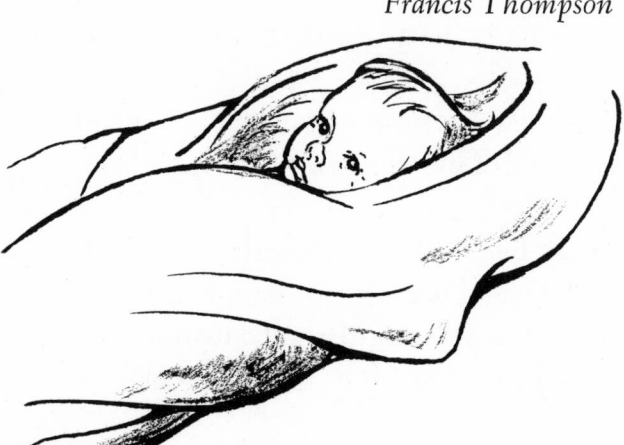

My Example

Lamb of God, I look to Thee;
Thou shalt my example be;
Thou art gentle, meek and mild;
Thou wast once a little child.

Loving Jesu, gentle Lamb,
In Thy gracious hands I am;
Make me, Saviour, what Thou art!
Live Thyself within my heart!

I shall then show forth Thy praise;
Serve Thee all my happy days;
Then the world shall always see
Christ, the Holy Child, in me.

Charles Wesley

A Child's Evening Prayer

Jesus, tender Shepherd, hear me,
  Bless Thy little lamb tonight;
Through the darkness be Thou near me,
  Keep me safe till morning light.

All this day Thy hand has led me,
  And I thank Thee for Thy care;
Thou hast clothed and warmed and fed me;
  Listen to my evening prayer.

Let my sins be all forgiven!
  Bless the friends I love so well!
Take me, when I die, to Heaven;
  Happy, there with Thee to dwell.

Mary Lundie Duncan

Bible Stories

The room was low and small and kind;
  And in its cupboard old,
The shells were set out to my mind;
  The cups I loved with rims of gold.

Then, with that good gift which she had,
  My mother showed at will,
David, the ruddy Syrian lad,
  With his few sheep upon a hill;

A shop down a rude country street,
  The chips strewn on the floor,
And faintly seen across the heat;
  The simple kinsfolk at the door;

Mary amid the homely din,
  As slim as violet;
The little Jesus just within,
  About His father's business set.

My mother rose, and then I knew
  As she stood smiling there,
Her gown was of that gentle blue
  Which she had made the Virgin wear.

How far the very chairs were grown!
    The gilt rose on each back,
Into a Syrian rose was blown,
    And not our humble gold and black.

That week long, in our acres old,
    Lad David did I see;
From out our cups with rims of gold,
    The little Jesus supped with me.

Lizette Woodworth Reese

EVENING PRAYER

She sang her little bedtime air
And drowsy-wise she spoke her prayer.

And as she spoke I saw the room
Open and stretch and glow and bloom;

And in her eyes I saw a ring
Of heaven's angels, listening.

Hermann Hagedorn

The Mother's Tale

Just before bed,
"Oh, one more story,
Mother!" they said;
And in the glory
Of red and gold
Beyond the fender
Their mother told
Splendor on splendor.

A small boy threw
A handful of seeds,
And a beanstalk grew
Faster than weeds
As high as heaven . . .
She wore a red hood . . .
Once there were seven
Dwarfs in a wood . . .

So the children found
A gingerbread house . . .
So Puss with a bound
Killed the Giant-mouse . . .
"Now, Mother, tell a
Best tale of all!"
So Cinderella
Went to the ball . . .

"Don't stop, Mother!"
It's time to rest.
"Oh, tell us another,
The very best!"
So the best of all
She told to them:
"Once in a stall
In Bethlehem . . ."

Eleanor Farjeon

CRADLE HYMN

Hush, my dear, lie still and slumber;
 Holy angels guard thy bed;
Heavenly blessings without number,
 Gently falling on thy head.

How much better thou'rt attended
 Than the Son of God could be,
When from heaven he descended
 And became a child like thee!

Soft and easy is thy cradle:
 Coarse and hard thy Saviour lay,
When his birthplace was a stable,
 And his softest bed was hay.

See the kindly shepherds round him,
 Telling wonders from the sky!
Where they sought him, there they found him,
 With his Virgin Mother by.

See the lovely babe a-dressing,
 Lovely infant, how he smiled,
When He wept, the mother's blessing
 Soothed and hushed the holy Child.

Lo, he slumbers in the manger,
   Where the horned oxen fed,
Peace, my darling, here's no danger,
   Here's no oxen near thy bed.

Isaac Watts

I Only Know a Glowing Warmth

I only know a glowing warmth,
And sweet, soft light above,
When Mother leans down o'er my bed,
And whispers, "God is Love."

I only know how I feel so safe,
So circled in His arm,
When Mother holds me close and says,
"Love keeps thee from all harm."

And when she goes and shuts the door,
Love watches with me still,
All radiant darkness so secure,
God keeps me from all ill.

Olive Beaupré Miller

PRAYER

Last night I crept across the snow,
Where only tracking rabbits go,
And then I waited quite alone
Until the Cristmas radiance shone!

At midnight twenty angels came,
Each white and shining like a flame.
At midnight twenty angels sang,
The stars swung out like bells and rang.

They lifted me across the hill,
They bore me in their arms until
A greater glory greeted them.
It was the town of Bethlehem.

And gently, then, they set me down,
All worshipping that holy town,
And gently, then, they bade me raise
My head to worship and to praise.

And gently, then, the Christ smiled down.
Ah, there was glory in that town!
It was as if the world were free
And glistening with purity.

And in that vault of crystal blue,
It was as if the world were new,
And myriad angels, file on file,
Gloried in the Christ Child's smile.

It was so beautiful to see
Such glory, for a child like me,
So beautiful, it does not seem
It could have been a Christmas Dream.

John Farrar

SONG

Why do bells of Christmas ring?
Why do little children sing?

Once a lovely shining star,
Seen by shepherds from afar,
Gently moved until its light
Made a manger's cradle bright.
There a darling baby lay
Pillowed soft upon the hay;
And its mother sung and smiled:
"This is Christ, the holy Child!"

Therefore bells for Christmas ring,
Therefore little children sing.

Eugene Field

For Christmas Day

A carol round the ruddy hearth,
  A song outside the door—
Let Christmas Day make sure its lay
  Sounds sweetly to the poor.

A turkey in the baking-tin,
  A pudding in the pot—
Let Christmas Day the hunger stay
  In them that have not got.

Red berries on the picture-frame,
  White berries in the hall—
Let Christmas Day look twice as gay
  With evergreens for all.

A stocking on the chimneypiece,
  A present on the chair—
Let Christmas Day not pass away
  Till those who have do share.

A star upon the midnight sky,
  A shepherd looking East—
On Christmas Day let all men pray,
  And not till after, feast.

Eleanor Farjeon

God bless your house this holy night,
  And all within it;

God bless the candle that you light
  To midnight's minute:

The board at which you break your bread,
  The cup you drink of:

And as you raise it, the unsaid
  Name that you think of:

The warming fire, the bed of rest,
  The ringing laughter:

These things, and all things else be blest
  From floor to rafter

This holy night, from dark to light,
  Even more than other

And, if you have no house to-night,
  God bless you, brother.

Eleanor Farjeon

CHRISTMASTIDE

Snow time, sad time,
   The world is growing old;
The shadows fall across the wall,
   The night is wan and cold;
When lo! the joyous songs arise
Of angels in the starry skies.

Child time, glad time,
   The world is young again;
The starlight streams, the holly gleams
   Upon the frosted pane,
Grant us, dear Lord, a place beside
The baby Christ, at Christmastide!

Willis Boyd Allen

An Ancient Christmas Carol

He came all so still
  Where His mother was,
As dew in April
  That falleth on the grass.

He came all so still
  Where His mother lay,
As dew in April
  That falleth on the spray.

He came all so still
  To His mother's bower
As dew in April
  That falleth on the flower.

Mother and maiden
  Was never none but she!
Well might such a lady
  God's mother be.

Unknown

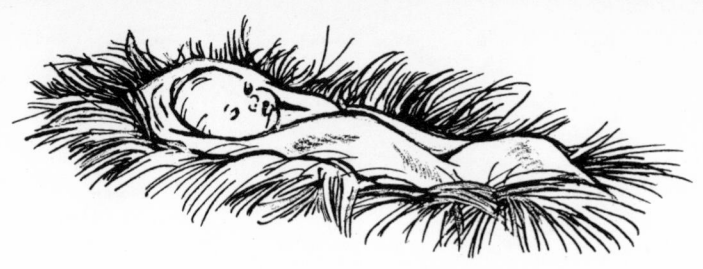

A Christmas Folk Song

The little Jesus came to town;
The wind blew up, the wind blew down;
Out in the street the wind was bold;
Now who would house Him from the cold?

Then opened wide the stable door,
Fair were the rushes on the floor;
The Ox put forth a horned head:
"Come, little Lord, here make Thy bed."

Up rose the Sheep were folded near;
"Thou Lamb of God, come, enter here."
He entered there to rush and reed,
Who was the Lamb of God indeed.

The little Jesus came to town;
With ox and sheep He laid Him down;
Peace to the byre, peace to the fold,
For that they housed Him from the cold!

Lizette Woodworth Reese

CHRISTMAS MORNING

If Bethlehem were here today,
  Or this were very long ago,
There wouldn't be a wintertime
  Nor any cold or snow.

I'd run out through the garden gate,
  And down along the pasture walk;
And off beside the cattle barns
  I'd hear a kind of gentle talk.

I'd move the heavy iron chain
  And pull away the wooden pin;
I'd push the door a little bit
  And tiptoe very softly in.

The pigeons and the yellow hens
  And all the cows would stand away;
Their eyes would open wide to see
  A lady in the manger hay,
If this were very long ago
  And Bethlehem were here today.

And Mother held my hand and smiled—
  I mean the lady would—and she
Would take the woolly blankets off
  Her little boy so I could see.

His shut-up eyes would be asleep,
  And he would look just like our John,
And he would be all crumpled, too,
  And have a pinkish color on.

I'd watch his breath go in and out.
  His little clothes would all be white.
I'd slip my finger in his hand
  To feel how he could hold it tight.

And she would smile and say, "Take care,"
  The mother, Mary, would "Take care;"
And I would kiss his little hand
  And touch his hair.

While Mary put the blankets back
  The gentle talk would soon begin.
And when I'd tiptoe softly out
  I'd meet the Wise Men going in.

Elizabeth Madox Roberts

How Far Is It to Bethlehem?

How far is it to Bethlehem?
　　Not very far.
Shall we find the stable-room
　　Lit by a star?

Can we see the little Child,
　　Is He within?
If we lift the wooden latch
　　May we go in?

May we stroke the creatures there,
　　Ox, ass, or sheep?
May we peep like them and see
　　Jesus asleep?

If we touch His tiny hand
　　Will He awake?
Will He know we've come so far
　　Just for His sake?

Great kings have precious gifts,
　　And we have naught;
Little smiles and little tears
　　Are all we brought.

For all weary children
  Mary must weep.
Here, on His bed of straw,
  Sleep, children, sleep.

God, in His Mother's arms
  Babes in the byre,
Sleep, as they sleep who find
  Their heart's desire.

Frances Chesterton

The First Night

The stable door was closed that night,
But through the cracks no bolts could bar
The light of holy innocence
Burst like a spraying star.

Even the beasts were glad He came.
They knelt in patience where He lay,
Content to yield for His baby head
Their evening meal of hay.

Louise Ayres Garnett

ONCE IN ROYAL DAVID'S CITY

Once in royal David's city
  Stood a lowly cattle shed,
Where a Mother laid her baby
  In a manger for His bed;
Mary was that Mother mild,
Jesus Christ her little child.

He came down to earth from heaven,
  Who is God and Lord of all,
And His shelter was a stable,
  And his cradle was a stall,
With the poor, and mean, and lowly
Lived on earth our Saviour Holy.

And through all His wondrous childhood,
    He would honor and obey,
Love and watch the lowly Maiden,
    In whose gentle arms He lay;
Christian children all must be
Mild, obedient, good as He.

For He is our childhood's pattern,
    Day by day like us He grew,
He was little, weak, and helpless,
    Tears and smiles like us He knew;
And He feeleth for our sadness,
And He shareth in our gladness.

And our eyes at last shall see Him,
    Through His own redeeming love,
For that Child so dear and gentle
    Is our Lord in heaven above;
And He leads His children on
To the place where He has gone.

Not in that poor lowly stable,
    With the oxen standing by,
We shall see Him; but in heaven,
    Set at God's right hand on high,
When like stars His children crowned
All in white shall wait around.

Cecil Frances Alexander

An Old Christmas Carol

As Joseph was a-waukin',
　He heard an angel sing,
"This night shall be the birthnight
　Of Christ our heavenly King.

"His birth-bed shall be neither
　In housen nor in hall,
Nor in the place of paradise,
　But in the oxen's stall.

"He neither shall be rocked
　In silver nor in gold,
But in the wooden manger
　That lieth in the mould.

"He neither shall be washen
　With white wine nor red,
But with the fair spring water
　That on you shall be shed.

"He neither shall be clothed
　In purple nor in pall,
But in the fair, white linen
　That usen babies all."

As Joseph was a-waukin',
  Thus did the angel sing,
And Mary's son at midnight
  Was born to be our King.

Then be you glad, good people
  At this time of the year;
And light you up your candles,
  For His star it shineth clear.

Anonymous

JUNIPER

Who does not love the juniper tree?
The scent of its branches comes back to me,
And ever I think of the Holy Three
Who came to rest by the juniper tree!
Joseph and Mary and little wee Son
Came to rest when the day was done!
And the little Child slept on His Mother's knee
In the shelter sweet of the juniper tree!

Eileen Duggan

A Carol for Sleepy Children

When Mary came to Bethlehem
on the first Christmas night,
she bore the lovely Christ Child
to be each child's delight.

There was no room in Bethlehem
for anyone so small
and yet so great as Mary's Child
but in an ox's stall.

There was no bed in Bethlehem
for anyone so poor
and yet so rich as Mary's Child
but on the stable floor.

O all you little children
who sleep in linen white
would you not share your cradles
if Jesus came tonight?

Sister Maris Stella

LONG, LONG AGO

Winds through the olive trees
   Softly did blow,
Round little Bethlehem
   Long, long ago.

Sheep on the hillside lay
   Whiter than snow;
Shepherds were watching them,
   Long, long ago.

Then from the happy sky,
   Angels bent low,
Singing their songs of joy,
   Long, long ago.

For in a manger bed,
   Cradled we know,
Christ came to Bethlehem,
   Long, long ago.

Anonymous

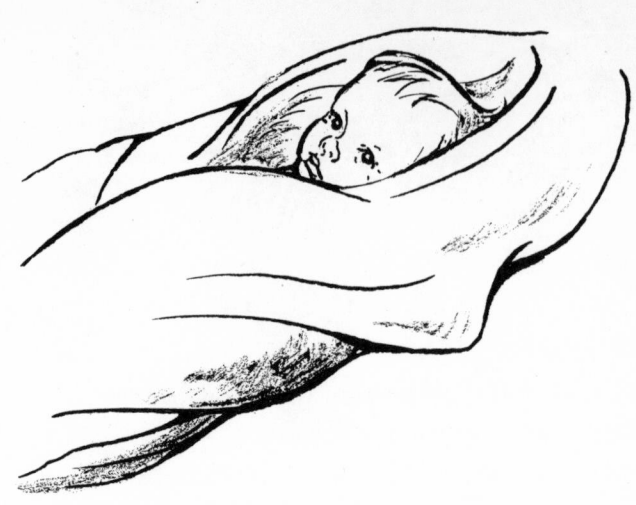

In the Stable

There was a pussy in the stable
When Christ was born.
There was an ox there and a donkey,
In the grey dawn.
But there was a pussy there also,
That Christmas morn.

And there was a mouse in the corner,
Still with surprise.
And by the door there was a brown dog,
Old and so wise.
He peeped through the fur on his forehead
With such bright eyes.

And there was a little bird there too,
With a red breast,
And with its beak it pulled out feathers
To make a nest,
To help Mary make for her Baby
A place to rest.

All the animals gave all they could
On Christmas day.
The ox and the ass gave their stable
And their sweet hay.
The pussy cat purred a lullaby
Loving and gay.

And the loyal old dog kept unsleeping
Watch by the door,
And the mouse kept so still in wonder
There on the floor.
Their service cried out to the Baby,
I love and adore.

They knew that He could not say thank you,
He was too weak,
Yet they knew He thanked them and loved them,
Humble and meek.
They knew He was God the Almighty
Come love to seek.

Elizabeth Goudge

CRADLE HYMN

Away in a manger, no crib for a bed,
The little Lord Jesus laid down His sweet head,
The stars in the bright sky looked down where He lay—
The little Lord Jesus asleep in the hay.

The cattle are lowing, the baby awakes,
But little Lord Jesus, no crying He makes.
I love thee, Lord Jesus! Look down from the sky,
And stay by my cradle till morning is nigh.

Martin Luther

Christmas Carol for the Dog

This is a carol for the dog
that long ago in Bethlehem
saw shepherds running towards the town
and followed them.

He trotted stiffly at their heels;
he sniffed the lambs that they were bringing;
he heard the herald angels sing,
yet did not know what they were singing.

With tail erect and tilted ears
he trotted through the stable door.
He saw the shepherds kneeling low
upon the floor.

He found Saint Joseph watching by
Our Lady with her newborn Boy,
and being only dog, he wagged
his tail for joy.

There stationed by the Baby's crib
he kept good guard through the long night,
with ears thrown back and muzzle high
and both eyes bright.

Sister Maris Stella

While Shepherds Watched

Like small curled feathers, white and soft,
  The little clouds went by,
Across the moon, and past the stars,
  And down the western sky:
In upland pastures, where the grass
  With frosted dew was white,
Like snowy clouds the young sheep lay,
  That first, best Christmas night.

The shepherds slept; and, glimmering faint,
  With twist of thin, blue smoke,
Only their fire's crackling flames
  The tender silence broke—
Save when a young lamb raised his head,
  Or, when the night wind blew,
A nesting bird would softly stir,
  Where dusky olives grew—

With finger on her solemn lip,
  Night hushed the shadowy earth,
And only stars and angels saw
  The little Saviour's birth;
Then came such flash of silver light
  Across the bending skies,
The wondering shepherds woke, and hid
  Their frightened dazzled eyes!

And all their gentle sleepy flock
  Looked up, then slept again,
Nor knew the light that dimmed the stars
  Brought endless peace to men—
Nor even heard the gracious words
  That down the ages ring—
"The Christ is born! the Lord has come,
  Good will on earth to bring!"

Then o'er the moonlit, misty fields,
  Dumb with the world's great joy,
The shepherds sought the white-walled town,
  Where lay the baby boy—
And oh, the gladness of the world,
  The glory of the skies,
Because the longed-for Christ looked up,
  In Mary's happy eyes!

Margaret Deland

Before the paling of the stars,
　Before the winter morn,
Before the earliest cockrow,
　Jesus Christ was born:
Born in a stable,
　Cradled in a manger,
In the world His hands had made
　Born a stranger.

Priest and king lay fast asleep
　In Jerusalem,
Young and old lay fast asleep
　In crowded Bethlehem;
Saint and Angel, ox and ass,
　Kept a watch together
Before the Christmas daybreak
　In the winter weather.

Jesus on His mother's breast
　In the stable cold,
Spotless Lamb of God was He,
　Shepherd of the fold:
Let us kneel with Mary maid,
　With Joseph bent and hoary,
With Saint and Angel, ox and ass,
　To hail the King of Glory.

Christina Rossetti

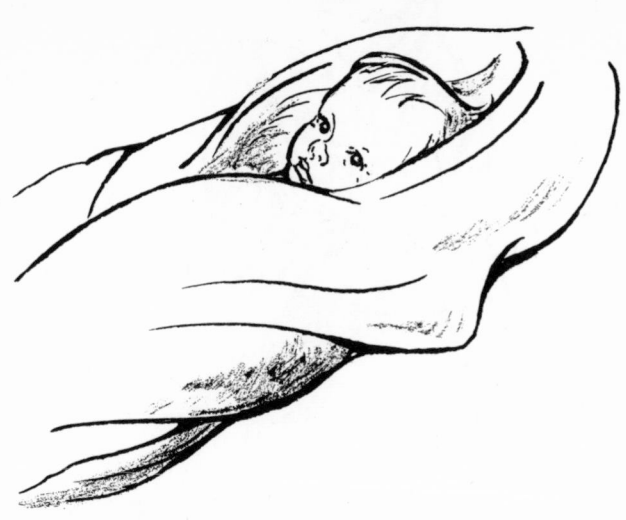

Spanish Lullaby

The poor Son of Mary,
   Cradle He had none;
His father was a carpenter,
   So he made Him one.

His father made a cradle
   Of wood he had found;
Mary Mother rocked Him,
   And then He slept sound.

You, too, sleep, my baby,
   Never you fear;
Mother is beside you,
   The Son of God is near.

Louis Untermeyer

The Mother's Song

She knew, the Maiden Mother knew,
Singing in the stable dim,
She sang for all the children who
Ever should come after Him;
Holding Him on either hand,
She knew they were not one and one,
But she was every mother and
He was every mother's son.

"Thou little thing, thou little thing!
All the joy of earth is thine.
More men's eyes shall shine for thee
Than stars shall in the heavens shine.

"Thou little thing, thou little thing!
To all sorrow art thou wed.
Men shall shed more tears for thee
Than heaven drops of rain shall shed.

"Thou little thing, thou little thing!
All things born thy name shall know.
More small tongues shall utter thee
Than daisies shall in meadows grow.

"Thou little thing, thou little thing!
All the world shall follow thee.
More souls shalt thou to heaven bring
Than birds shall fly from sea to sea.

"Thou little thing, thou little thing!
Each death is thine, and every birth.
Thou shalt more often live and die
Than all the peoples of the earth."

She knew, the Maiden Mother knew,
When she sang her child to sleep,
She sang for all the mothers who
Ever had a child in keep.
Lulling him upon her breast,
She knew, as she that burden bore,
She all children sang to rest
With her own for evermore.

Eleanor Farjeon

A LILY OF THE FIELD

In all his glory, Solomon
    Was never so arrayed;
Yet far more beautiful is one—
    A Mother and a Maid—
Whose loveliness and lowliness
God stooped from highest Heaven to bless.

John Bannister Tabb

The Ox and the Donkey's Carol

The Christ Child lay in the ox's stall,
the stars shone great and the stars shone small,
but one bright star outshone them all.

The cattle stood in the cleanly straw
and strange to them was the sight they saw.
The ox and the donkey watched with awe.

The shepherds ran from the uplands wide,
the sheepbells tinkled, the angels cried
joy to the dreaming countryside.

The three kings bowed at the stable door,
their raiment trailed on the dusty floor.
They saw the sight they had journeyed for.

The kings came last in a lordly throng.
The shepherds ran in the space of a song,
but the beasts had been there all night long.
    Noel   Noel   Noel

Sister Maris Stella

The Riding of the Kings

In a far land upon a day,
Where never snow did fall,
Three Kings went riding on the way
Bearing presents all.

And one wore red, and one were gold,
And one was clad in green,
And one was young, and one was old,
And one was in between.

The middle one had human sense,
The young had loving eyes,
The old had much experience,
And all of them were wise.

Choosing no guide by eve and morn
But heaven's starry drifts,
They rode to find the Newly-Born
For whom they carried gifts.

Oh, far away in time they rode
Upon their wanderings,
And still in story goes abroad
The riding of the Kings.

So wise, that in their chosen hour,
As through the world they filed,
They sought not wealth or place or power,
But rode to find a Child.

Eleanor Farjeon

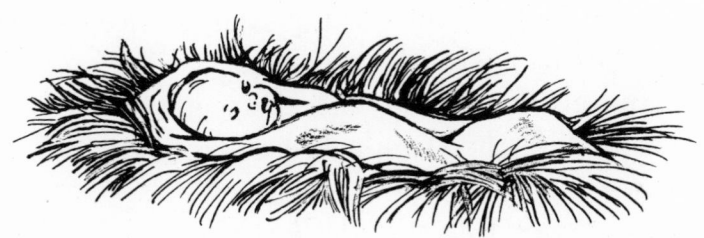

The Christ Child

The Christ Child lay on Mary's lap,
  His hair was like a light.
(O weary, weary were the world,
  But here is all aright.)

The Christ Child lay on Mary's breast,
  His hair was like a star.
(O stern and cunning are the kings,
  But here the true hearts are.)

The Christ Child lay on Mary's heart,
  His hair was like a fire.
(O weary, weary is the world,
  But here the world's desire.)

The Christ Child stood at Mary's knee,
  His hair was like a crown,
And all the flowers looked up at Him,
And all the stars looked down.

Gilbert Keith Chesterton

At Easter Time

The little flowers came through the ground,
    At Easter time, at Easter time;
They raised their heads and looked around,
    At happy Easter time.
And every pretty bud did say,
    "Good people, bless this holy day,
For Christ is risen, the angels say
    At happy Easter time!"

The pure white lily raised its cup
    At Easter time, at Easter time;
The crocus to the sky looked up
    At happy Easter time.
"We'll hear the song of Heaven!" they say,
    "Its glory shines on us today.
Oh! may it shine on us alway
    At holy Easter time!"

'Twas long and long and long ago,
   That Easter time, that Easter time;
But still the pure white lilies blow
   At happy Easter time,
And still each little flower doth say,
   "Good Christians, bless this holy day,
For Christ is risen, the angels say
   At blessed Easter time!"

Laura E. Richards

AN EASTER CAROL

   Spring bursts today,
For Christ is risen and all the earth's at play.
   Flash forth, thou Sun.
The rain is over and gone, its work is done.

   Winter is past,
Sweet spring is come at last, is come at last.
   Bud, fig, and vine,
Bud, olive, fat with fruit and oil and wine.

Break forth this morn
In roses, thou but yesterday a thorn.
Uplift thy head,
O pure white lily through the winter dead.

Beside your dams
Leap and rejoice, you merrymaking lambs.
All herds and flocks
Rejoice, all beasts of thickets and of rocks.

Sing, creatures, sing,
Angels and men and birds and everything.

Christina Rossetti

O Bells in the Steeple

O bells in the steeple,
Ring out to all people
That Christ has arisen—that Easter is here!
Touch heaven's blue ceiling
With your happy pealing;
O bells in the steeple, ring out full and clear!

May Riley Smith

INDEXES

INDEX OF AUTHORS

Alexander, Cecil Frances 58, 112
Allen, Willis Boyd 105

Blake, William 12, 35, 38, 42, 44, 46, 55
Bone, Florence 78
Borie, Lysbeth Boyd 87
Brown, Alice 22
Browning, Elizabeth Barrett 68
Browning, Robert 11
Buchanan, Fannie R. 10

Cane, Melville 52
Carlyle, Thomas 29
Chesterton, Frances 110
Chesterton, Gilbert Keith 132
Clarke, Thomas Curtis 65
Coleridge, Samuel Taylor 64
Conkling, Hilda 11, 45
Coolidge, Susan 26

Davies, Mary Carolyn 9
Davies, W. H. 13
Deland, Margaret 122
deVere, Sir Audrey 64
Dickinson, Emily 60
Duggan, Eileen 115
Duncan, Mary Lundie 93

Farjeon, Eleanor 32, 96, 103, 104, 126, 130
Farrar, John 100
Field, Eugene 102
Fyleman, Rose 9

Gale, Norman 22, 86
Garnett, Louise Ayres 111
Goudge, Elizabeth 24, 76, 118

Hagedorn, Hermann 95
Hinkson, Katharine Tynan 43
Hodgson, Ralph 80
Hopkins, J. G. E. 56
Hugo, Victor 73

Johnstone, Henry 73

Loftus, Cecilia 15
Lord, Daniel A. 12, 72, 85
Luke, Jemima 81
Luther, Martin 120

Markham, Edwin 71
Martin, John 74
Miller, Olive Beaupré 99
Morley, Christopher 54

Orleans, Ilo 85

Reese, Lizette Woodworth 55, 94, 107
Richards, Laura E. 133
Roberts, Elizabeth Maddox 108
Rossetti, Christina 23, 36, 61, 124, 134

Setoun, Gabriel 66, 73
Sister Maris Stella 116, 121, 129
Smith, May Riley 136
Smith, William Hawley 14
Stephens, James 40, 47

Tabb, John Bannister 17, 128
Taylor, Ann and Jane 79
Taylor, Jane 70
Teasdale, Sara 41
Tennyson, Alfred, Lord 30
Thayer, Mary Dixon 20
Thompson, Francis 89
Turner, Nancy Byrd 31

Untermeyer, Louis 125

Van Dyke, Henry 34, 35

Watts, Isaac 98
Webb, Thomas H. B. 83
Wesley, Charles 88, 92
Wynne, Annette 16, 18, 35, 50

Ancient Christmas Carol, An   106
Ancient Prayer, An   83
Angel, An   84
Angel Singing, An   12
Arbor Day   16
At Easter Time   133
Auguries of Innocence   55

Before the Paling of the Stars   124
Bible Stories   94
Boats Sail on the Rivers   23

Carol for Sleepy Children, A   116
Child's Evening Prayer, A   93
Child's Thought of God, A   68
Christ Child, The   132
Christmas Carol for the Dog   121
Christmas Folk Song, A   107
Christmas Morning   108
Christmastide   105
Country Faith, The   22
Cradle Hymn   98
Cradle Hymn   120
Crayons   54
Creation, The   58

Day before April, The   9
Do You Know How Many Stars?   36

Eagle on the Mountain Crest   45
Easter Carol, An   134
Evening Hymn   80
Evening Hymn for a Little Family   79
Evening Prayer   95
Ex Ore Infantium   89
Example, The   13
Eyes of God, The   73

Fern Song   17
First Night, The   111
Flower in the Crannied Wall   30
Fog, the Magician   52
For Christmas Day   103
Four Things   35

God Careth   28
God Giveth All Things   82
God Is Everywhere   19
God Is So Good   70
God's Dark   74
God's Gift   82
God's House   18
God's Providence   31
Golden Rule, The   35
Good Night   73
Good Night Prayer   73
Guardian Angel   76

He Prayeth Best   64
How Far Is It to Bethlehem?   110
How Nice!   20

I Never Saw a Moor   60
I Only Know a Glowing Warmth   99
I Will Give You   35
If All the Skies   34
In the Morning   15
In the Stable   118
It Was Saint Francis Who Came   50

Joy   11
Juniper   115
Just for Jesus   87

Lamb, The   44
Lily of the Field, A   128
Little Song of Life, A   55
Long, Long Ago   117
Loving Jesus   88
Lullaby   84

Moon, The   39
Mother's Song, The   126
Mother's Tale, The   96
My Example   92
Mystery, The   80

Night   38
Night   41

O Bells in the Steeple   136
Old Christmas Carol, An   114
Once in Royal David's City   112
Out in the Fields with God   21
Ox and the Donkey's Carol, The
  129

Paradise   61
Poem for a Child   56
Prayer for a Child   14
Prayer   100
Prayer, A   71
Prayer for a Little Home, A   78

Rain   85
Reality   64
Revelation   22
Riding of the Kings, The   130
Round the Clock   72

Search, The   65
Sheep and Lambs   43
Singing Time   9
Song   102

Song in Praise of the Lord, A   37
Spanish Lullaby   125
Spring   12
Stars, The   36
Sweet Story of Old   81

Tardy Playmate, The   10
Thanks   86
Thanksgiving for the Earth   24
Things to Remember   42
This Holy Night   104
Tiger, The   46
Time to Go   26
Today   29

Voice of God, The   47

While Shepherds Watched   122
Whisperer, The   40
Who Taught Them?   49
Wildflowers   32
World's Music, The   66

Year's at the Spring, The   11

INDEX OF FIRST LINES

A carol round the ruddy hearth   103
A robin redbreast in a cave   42
All happy and glad in the sunshine I stood   12
All in the April morning   43
All things bright and beautiful   58
An Angel came as I lay in bed   84
As Joseph was a-waukin'   114
Away in a manger, no crib for a bed   120

Before the paling of the stars   124
Bless my friends, the whole world bless   73
Boats sail on the rivers   23

Dance to the beat of the rain, little Fern   17
Do you know how many stars   36
Down in the meadow, spread with dew   22

Flower in the crannied wall   30
For life and health and strength   82
Four things a man must learn to do   35
Fourteen angels round my head   84

Give me a good digestion, Lord, and also something to digest   83
Glad that I live am I   55
God bless your house this holy night   104
God gives so many lovely things!   31
God is so good that He will hear   70
God send us a little home   78
God watches o'er us all day   73
Good morning, sky   10
Good night! Good night!   73
God's house is wide and very tall   18

He came all so still   106
He came and took me by the hand   80
He prayeth best who loveth best   64
Here in the country's heart   22
Here's an example from   13
His bronze shown like a haze   45
How far is it to Bethlehem?   110
How nice it is, dear God, to know   20
Hush, my dear, lie still and slumber   98

I bent unto the ground   47
I hear no voice, I feel no touch   80

I heard an Angel singing   12
I never saw a moor   60
I only know a glowing warmth   99
I see the moon   39
I sought his love in sun and stars   65
I thank you, God   85
I think when I read that sweet story of old   81
I wake in the morning early   9
I will give you the end of a golden string   35
If all the skies were sunshine   34
If Bethlehem were here today   108
In a far land upon a day   130
In all his glory, Solomon   128
It was Saint Francis who came   50

Jesus, I kneel down to say   87
Jesus, tender Shepherd, hear me   93
Joy is not a thing you can see   11
Just before bed   96

Lamb of God, I look to Thee   92
Last night I crept across the snow   100
Like small curled feathers, white and soft   122
Little Jesus, wast Thou shy   89
Little Lamb, who made thee?   44
Love thy God and love Him only   64
Loving Jesus, meek and mild   88

Now condescend, Almighty King   79

O bells in the steeple   136
On Arbor Day   16
Once in a dream I saw the flowers   61
Once in royal David's city   112
Over in the corner there's a Person standing   76

Praised be our Lord for our brother the sun   24

She knew, the Maiden Mother knew   126
She sang her little bedtime air   95
Since rain is good for crops in May   85
Sky so bright   37
Snow time, sad time   105
So here hath been dawning   29
Something around which it may twine   28
Spring bursts today   134
Stars over snow   41

143

Teach me, Father, how to go   71
Thank you very much indeed   86
The Christ Child lay in the ox's stall   129
The Christ Child lay on Mary's lap   132
The dark is kind and cozy   74
The day before April   9
The golden Rule is the Rule of Three   35
The little cares that fretted me   21
The little flowers came through the ground   133
The little Jesus came to town   107
The moon was round   40
The poor Son of Mary   125
The rabbit came bounding   56
The room was low and small and kind   94
The stable door was closed that night   111
The sun descending in the West   38
The world's a very happy place   67
The year's at the spring   11
There was a pussy in the stable   118
There's not a tint that paints the rose   19
They know the time to go!   26
They say that God lives very high!   68
This is a carol for the dog   121
Tiger, tiger, burning bright   46
To see the world in a grain of sand   55

Up in the morning, out of bed   72

We mustn't pick the garden flowers   32
We thank our loving Father God   82
What do the stars do   36
When, in the morning, fresh from sleep   15
When it gets dark the birds and flowers   14
When Mary came to Bethlehem   116
Who does not love the juniper tree?   115
Who taught the bird to build her nest   49
Why do bells of Christmas ring?   102
Winds through the olive trees   117
Wrapped in a cloak   52

You ask me how God felt on that first day   54